KTG know the game

Lifesaving and Water Safety

Produced in collaboration with
The Royal Life Saving Society

Published by A & C Black (Publishers) Ltd
35 Bedford Row, London WC1R 4JH

Contents

Foreword

The Royal Life Saving Society

The Royal Life Saving Society was established in 1891 with the specific aim of reducing the annual death toll caused by drowning. The Society embarked upon this task in the following three ways:

1 By providing information and advice on the prevention of water accidents.
2 By teaching water rescue and resuscitation skills.
3 By providing a voluntary lifeguard service, co-ordinating over 100 registered lifeguard clubs, to help make all types of waterways, both at the coast and inland, far safer places.

To encourage people to acquire the necessary knowledge and skill the Society has developed various awards schemes (see the Teaching Programmes chart inside the back cover). The information in this book should help you prepare for the AQUAPACK Awards which include Water Safety, Basic Resuscitation, Aquanaut, Rescue Skills and Safer Swimming awards.

It will also help towards preparations for the RLSS Elementary and Intermediate Awards which provide an introduction to the more complex lifesaving skills. These are tested in the RLSS Bronze Medallion which is the basic test of a qualified lifesaver who must show acceptable standards of knowledge, judgement, technique and physical ability. Further details of the Bronze Medallion and all the Society's Awards can be found in "The Awards Schemes", Section 6 of the *RLSS Handbook*.

The RLSS is a Commonwealth-wide organisation with a Branch or Representative in almost all Commonwealth countries. In the vast majority of non-Commonwealth countries there are national lifesaving organisations that have a similar structure and organisations to the RLSS.

Everyone should learn to be a lifesaver. For details of your local club or class ask at your local swimming baths, or the Society's Headquarters.

Introduction

Every year up to eight hundred people die by drowning in the British Isles. Almost one-quarter of these are children.

Most of these tragedies could be prevented if everyone understood the principles of water safety, water rescue and resuscitation.

The intention of this book is to outline some of the information and skills relating to the following elements of water safety and lifesaving:

1 **Water Safety**

Every year water activities are becoming more and more popular, with increasing numbers of people taking part in activities such as sailing, water ski-ing and board sailing. Furthermore, statistics show that a large number of deaths occur in the five- to fourteen-year-old age group.

It is neither practical nor desirable to deny people the opportunity to participate in water activites, but *everyone* should learn the rules of safety in and around water.

2 **Safer swimming**

One of the first principles of water safety is that everyone should learn how to swim. However, it is not sufficient merely to learn to swim a number of lengths in the relative safety of a swimming pool, as this may lead to a false confidence in one's own ability.

It is important that everyone becomes a safer swimmer by learning the skills and knowledge necessary to be able to deal with any difficulties which may arise in a variety of aquatic environments.

3 Helping others

Most drownings occur inland. Statistics suggest that over one-half of these drownings occur within three metres of safety. Furthermore, the vast majority of rescues are made by a member of the family, a friend or a member of the general public. If everyone were able to effect a simple reaching or throwing rescue the number of drownings would be substantially reduced.

4 Resuscitation and aftercare

It is sometimes not sufficient to bring a casualty to the shore as they may become unconscious and stop breathing. Therefore an important part of life saving is resuscitation, that is, the act of revival of an apparently dead person. The form of resuscitation which has proved to be most effective is Expired Air Resuscitation, the technique commonly referred to as 'the Kiss of Life'.

Expired Air Resuscitation is a skill which is useful not only in aquatic accidents but also in emergencies at home, work or in a variety of leisure activities.

Water safety

Many people are attracted to games and activities both in and around water. Children are particularly attracted to water, whether it be the sea, fast flowing rivers, garden ponds or puddles in the street. It is true that the majority of drownings occur where the water is deep enough for swimming, for example in rivers or the sea. Nevertheless it is a fallacy to presume that drownings occur only where it is possible to swim. Each year people, particularly children, drown in a wide variety of seemingly harmless locations, for example the domestic bath, paddling pools, garden ponds, streams or even washing machines. Indeed, in 1983 the domestic bath was responsible for the fourth highest incidence of drownings in the United Kingdom – higher than canals, docks and swimming pools – a figure which is probably equally applicable in other countries. It is therefore vital that everyone, particularly parents with young children, knows and understands the rules of water safety. What follows outlines those rules when around the home, out and about, swimming or boating.

Around the home

Many drowning accidents occur in and around the home when people feel at their safest, and this is particularly true with respect to children. Accidents can happen while housework is being done, when an unexpected visitor arrives or while the unsuspecting parent is relaxing for a moment. At such times a child may fill the bath and fall in, slip in the garden pond or fall head-first into a washing machine full of water. Here are some precautions which can help the home become a safer place.

Always supervise children at play near water

1 Never leave young children alone in the bath. Always check on older children and elderly people at regular intervals; they can easily slip, be knocked unconscious and drown.
2 Keep bath plugs out of the reach of small children since they soon learn how to put them in and turn on the taps.
3 Do not leave water unsupervised in open topped containers, such as buckets, sinks and washing-up bowls. People can drown in as little as 5 centimetres of water.
4 Always cover fishponds with chicken wire or nylon mesh as it is easy to overbalance and fall in.
5 Never leave children unsupervised near water. Even paddling pools are dangerous; always empty them as soon as the children have finished.
6 If you have a private swimming pool ensure that it is fenced to deter people from swimming on their own.
7 Ensure that garden gates are kept closed to prevent children from wandering off and falling into local streams or ponds.

Out and about

There are a number of occasions when one may be faced with potential water hazards out and about, when taking part in water sports or fishing, or merely taking a stroll in the countryside. It is important to be aware not only of the hazards but also of how to act in case of emergency (see further on p. 9, Safer Swimming). The following points outline how to take care when 'out and about'.

1 Water sports

If you wish to participate in water sports be sure that you learn from the experts. Join a club to learn the safe methods of taking part and always use the correct equipment. This will minimise the possibility of an accident.

2 Parking the car

Always park your car parallel to the water's edge on jetties, cliff tops or docks. A number of drownings occur each year because drivers park their cars carelessly and they roll into the water.

Choose a safe place to fish

3 Ice

During cold weather ponds and canals become frozen over. It may be tempting to go on the ice but it is often unsafe to do so. The shock of falling through the ice into cold water may cause unconsciousness and so make self-help impossible. Anyone who falls through the ice may also be carried under by the current and may not be able to break through to the surface.

4 Fishing

Never fish alone, it is all too easy to slip and fall in the water; always tell someone where you are going and what time you expect to return. Don't stand too close to river banks as they often have crumbling, unsafe edges, and always heed flood warnings since slowly-flowing rivers and streams can quickly become fast-moving.

5 When at play

Keep an eye on children – they can drown in very small ponds which are often disguised with weeds. A farm's slurry pit is also a point of danger; it contains soft mud but looks deceptively solid. Do not build, or play on, home-made rafts; they often come apart and are almost impossible to steer.

Beware home-made rafts

Bathe in the centre of a beach

Swimming

Swimming, whether it is in the comparative safety of the swimming pool or in open water, is becoming more and more popular every year. Such places are often the scene of unfortunate accidents when someone showing off attempts something beyond his capabilities and fails. Safety when swimming can be divided into two categories.

1 **Open water**
It is always important before swimming in open water to find out where it is safe to bathe. Red over yellow flags indicate areas which are patrolled by lifeguards; bathe between them. Never bathe where a red flag is flying; this indicates that conditions are dangerous. Places to avoid when swimming in open water include those near rocks, piers, breakwaters, and where people are riding surfboards or water ski- ing. When swimming in the sea always swim parallel to the shore as it is easy to be carried far out and distances in open water can often be deceptive. Do not dive into unknown waters; they may have rocks or rubbish below the surface.

2 **Swimming pools**
Swimming pools are comparatively less dangerous than open water as they are watched by lifeguards, but you should always take heed of their advice as it

is their job to prevent accidents. Do not run around the poolside as it is easy to fall in and injure yourself or others. Similarly, always ensure that the water is clear before jumping in, and never push someone else into the water – they may hit their head on the side or bottom of the pool, or hurt someone else. Before diving in, check the depth markings on the poolside and ensure it is deep enough to dive safely. If you *must* wear goggles ensure that they are made

Do not run around the poolside

to recognised standards, as badly made goggles can injure the eyes.

Boating

Before going afloat make sure that you know how to handle the craft; many accidents are caused by lack of preparation, so learn from the experts. If going on a long trip leave word of where you are going and your estimated time of return. Always be sure that you can swim at least fifty metres in the clothing you will be wearing while on the boat, and do not wear wellingtons or overload the boat. There are also some specific points which you should consider with respect to different types of craft.

1 **Houseboats/narrowboats**
   Make sure children and non-swimmers *always* wear lifejackets made to recognised standards (look for the kite mark in the United Kingdom) and ensure that they are fastened correctly. It is important to restrict young children by an approved safety harness and everyone should wear non-slip footwear to avoid slipping on wet surfaces. Do not forget to learn the man overboard drills.

2 **Yachts/sailing**
   Everyone should wear warm clothing and a lifejacket which is made to recognised standards and

fastens correctly. Learn both the man overboard and capsize drill, and if the boat cannot be righted stay with it. Stow all gear safely and before leaving on a trip do not forget to check the weather conditions.

3   Canoeing
Always canoe with at least two other people and learn emergency procedures, particularly how to perform an Eskimo Roll. Always wear a lifejacket or a buoyancy aid and helmet.

Canoe safely

Safer swimming

While the first principle of water safety is 'learn to swim' it is not sufficient to learn how to swim a number of lengths in the comparative safety and warmth of a swimming pool. The vast majority of drownings occur in open water where distances can be deceptive and the water very cold. What is more, there are many other hazards, for example currents, undertows, weirs, and weeds. Being a safer swimmer involves learning a bank of skills and knowledge upon which one may draw – for example, entries, surface diving, cold water survival techniques and understanding the action one should take in situations which hold particular dangers. This section deals with both safer swimming techniques and the action to be taken in special cases.

Entering the water

Slide-in entry
If water conditions are unknown a cautious 'feet first slide-in' is safest, as it is controlled and the feet can feel for any unseen obstacles. Always take care to lower the body into the water slowly and feel around for the bottom. If your feet do not touch the bottom swim very carefully.

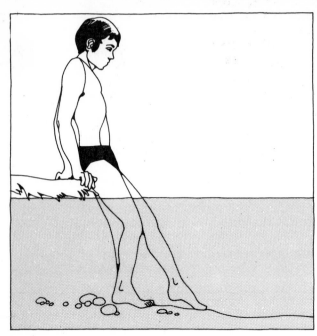

Slide-in entry

Step-in entry

Step-in entry

This should be used when jumping from a height of more than one metre into deep water. Take off with one foot leading, ensuring that when in the air the body is vertical and the legs together, with the arms crossed. Upon entry brake by depressing your arms and kicking your legs.

Straddle jump

This should be used from low height (up to one metre) into deep water, when minimum submergence is required.

Step out across the water with your arms spread out, leaning slightly forward with legs split fore and aft. Brake on entry by depressing your arms and closing your legs.

Straddle jump

Swimming skills

Side stroke

This is a very economical stroke due to the underwater recovery and is therefore very useful in rough water or when conserving energy. It is also used extensively in towing methods.

Glide position: lie on one side with the face resting in the water. The leading arm is extended fully beyond the head with the palm downwards and the trailing arm along the side of the body.

Arm action: pull through the water with the leading arm using a shallow semi-circular sweep. At the same

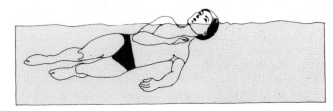

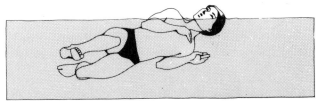

Side stroke

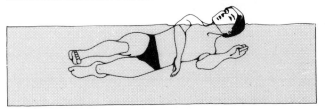

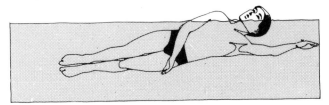

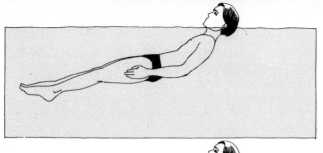

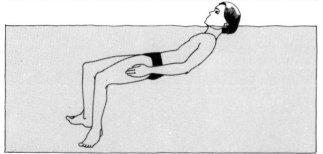

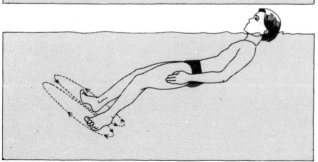

time bend the trailing arm to the chest. Glide forward with the leading arm at the same time pushing backward with the trailing arm.

Leg action: use a scissor kick parallel to the surface.

Co-ordination: the kick occurs when the leading arm glides forward.

Lifesaving backstroke

This is a very useful stroke for keeping the head clear of the water; it is also a basic element of advanced life saving techniques. You should lie on your back in the water, head slightly forward and the body sloping towards the feet. The legs should be dropped from the knee and the feet turned out. Kick back in a symmetrical and circular motion, bringing the knees and feet together. The stroke should be smooth and continuous.

Lifesaving backstroke

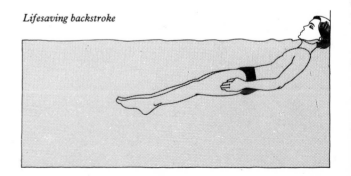

Special water skills

Treading water

This is a very important skill as it enables swimmers to stay as near as possible to a given point and to keep energy expenditure to a minimum. The legs are used to support the body and maintain the head position above the surface. The arms are used for balance. There are four types of kick from which one can choose: breast stroke; scissor kick; cycling; egg beater (alternate breast stroke leg action).

Feet first surface dive

This skill is necessary for avoiding an obstruction on the surface, for example an oil slick, or to collect something from the bottom. It is the safest method of surface diving and should be used in unknown conditions.

Tread water over the spot where you wish to submerge. Use a strong breast stroke kick and press down with the hands to raise the body high out of the water. Keep your legs together and hands by your side and as the head submerges pull your arms upwards to help you under.

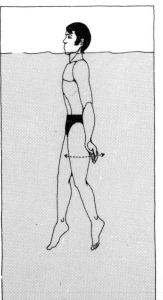
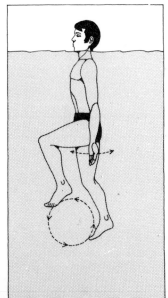
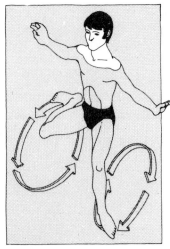

Treading water

Head first surface dive

When in clear water the head first surface dive can be used to avoid any obstruction on the surface. It is particularly useful as it can be performed from a swimming position.

Swim to a position two metres short of where you wish to dive. Bend your head and shoulders down sharply into the water. Lift your legs clear of the water and use a breast stroke arm action to pull down.

Climbing out

It is important to be able to cope with leaving the water where no steps or other aids are available, whether in deep or shallow water.

Place your hands firmly on the bank. If in shallow water push or jump from the bottom, in deep water kick vigorously, and lift your body clear of the water until your arms are straight. Rest one knee on the side, lean forward, lift the other leg and stand up.

Head first surface dive

  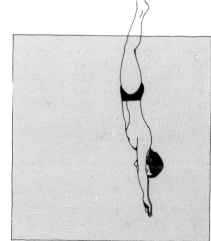

Action in special cases

Immersion in cold water

Immersion in cold water is known to be a major factor in most drownings at any time of the year. It may quickly bring about the state known as hypothermia, that is when the whole body is chilled to a much lower temperature than normal, below 35°C compared with the normal 37°C.

The symptoms of hypothermia are:

1. Unexpected, unreasonable and unco-operative behaviour.
2. Discomfort and pain.
3. Twitching.
4. Slurring of speech.
5. Mental and physical lethargy with failure to understand instructions.
6. Failure of, or abnormality in, vision.
7. Numbness or cramp.
8. Severe state of shock.
9. Irregular heart beat.
10. Violent outbursts of unexpected energy, violent language.

Not all of these symptoms may be present.

It is very important to prevent the casualty suffering further heat loss. The most dangerous moments occur when the casualty has been removed from the water, and it is important that he is protected from the wind and rain if possible.

What to do: gently dry off wet clothing and wrap the casualty up in blankets or get him into a sleeping bag, ideally with others in and around the bag generating warmth. If there is nothing dry with which to wrap him up, cover him with any available vegetation (e.g. bracken, ferns, grass, leaves etc.).

For those who can swallow, sugar should be taken in an easily digestible form (e.g. condensed milk). If possible, *send for help immediately* but do not leave the casualty alone.

The temperature of the inner core of the body *must not be disturbed* as the resulting sudden surge of warm blood to the surface of the body could be fatal. Therefore the following treatment *must not* be used: local heating, rubbing the skin, drinking alcohol or hot drinks.

If you find yourself in cold water
1. Do not panic.
2. Float quietly clinging to supportive objects. The Heat Escape Lessening Posture (HELP) is particularly effective in preventing the loss of body heat.
3. Even exceptionally strong swimmers may be overcome by shock and cold within very short distances, often as little as fifty metres.

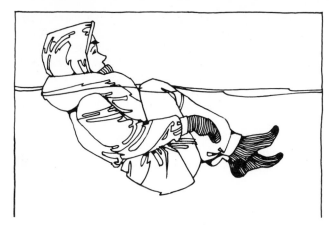

The Heat Escape Lessening Posture (HELP)

4   Do *not* remove clothing, except for heavy top coats and boots.

If you fall through ice
1   Call for help.
2   Spread your arms across the surface of the ice.
3   Kick to a swimming position and slide onto the ice.
4   Stay lying down and work your way to safety.

If someone else falls through ice
1   Send for help.
2   Avoid going on weakened ice.
3   Try to reach the casualty with a rope and pull to safety.
4   If you have to go on the ice lie flat and move cautiously. Use a ladder or similar method of spreading your weight across the ice.

The casualty who has fallen through ice will need special care. When you reach land follow the procedure for treating hypothermia outlined above.

Rescue over ice

Surf and rip tides

It is particularly dangerous to swim in surf. The unexpected strength of the breaking waves may take your legs, unbalance you and cause you to lose your footing. If this happens turn to face the shore, let the wave carry you in and swim between each one until you can safely stand.

A further danger is the channel returning the water to the open sea; this is called a rip tide. If caught in a rip tide you will be swept out to sea very rapidly. Never try to swim against the rip. Always swim parallel to the shore and back in on the surf.

Cars falling in water

Should your car fall into the water there may be a short time when it settles on the surface; every attempt should be made in this time to get out.

The car will sink engine first and if you are still in the car when it sinks keep calm and –
1   Wind up all windows.
2   Switch on lights to guide rescuers.
3   *Do not* try to open the doors too soon.
4   Lift children into the air pocket.
5   When the water reaches chin level the pressure inside and out will be equalised. Take a deep breath and try and force the door open. If this fails wind the windows down and you should now be able to open the door.
6   If there is more than one in the car, link hands and go out in a human chain to make sure no one is left behind. If you are the only competent lifesaver in the car be the last out.

Weirs

If drawn into a weir attempt to get to the bottom of the weir by diving down, and hold your breath until you are thrown to the surface.

Quicksand or deep mud

Do not try to stand up and walk. Spread your weight by lying flat on the surface and move by slow arm and leg actions.

Underwater weeds

Weeds will float apart if you move slowly, so avoid sudden movement. Swim very gently with a long slow breast or side stroke with minimal leg movements. The technique of 'sculling' can be useful.

The 999 drill

You do *not* need coins to make an emergency call. Lift the receiver, dial 999, and the operator will ask:—

1 which service you require

2 your telephone number.

You ask for the **Police** (or the **Coastguard** if near the coast). The Police or Coastguard will then ask you:—

1 what the trouble is

2 where it is

3 whether anyone is capable of taking action while help is arriving

4 the telephone number you are speaking from

5 your name and address.

By knowing what the questions will be and being able to answer them you will speed the arrival of the emergency services.

Helping others

Most drowning accidents occur in places which are not supervised or protected, for example canals, rivers and gravel pits. Over fifty per cent of all inland drownings occur within three metres of safety. Therefore it is often the ordinary bystander, be he a swimmer or non-swimmer, using his own initiative, who may be in a position to prevent a tragedy. Through regular training it is possible to develop one's ability to make safe and effective rescues.

No two drowning accidents are ever identical. For this reason each and every emergency has to be assessed on its own merits. An understanding of the principles of alertness, assessment, and action will help you to assess each emergency quickly and efficiently and carry out a safe and effective rescue.

Alertness

Drowning accidents happen suddenly and are not expected. Even a trained lifesaver may only perform an actual rescue once or twice in a lifetime, unless he is a lifeguard. However, even an untrained rescuer, providing he is alert, can recognise someone in distress and provide positive help. The following are examples of what might happen:

1 A child may slip on a river bank and fall in.
2 A group of children may slip off a home-made raft.
3 A fisherman may slip over and be carried down river by the current.
4 A swimmer may be carried out to sea very quickly on a rip tide.

Contrary to popular belief, people who are drowning do not all assume the same characteristics. The illustration opposite explains the main categories of drowning casualty which might be encountered. An understanding of the characteristics of each category may help you to identify someone who is in difficulty in a crowded bathing area. It will also help you to decide the best method of effecting a rescue.

Assessment – think before you act

Whatever the degree of skill of the person who identifies a dangerous situation, correct assessment is vital. If the wrong action is taken the result may be fatal for both the rescuer and the casualty.

Many factors may afffect the plan of action; for example your own skill and experience, the number of casualties and their condition, the aids available, the environmental conditions and the places of entry and exit (if it is necessary to enter the water).

The time spent on assessment may vary considerably, from the almost instant (e.g. reaching out to grasp a casualty close to the bank) to the preparation of a deliberate plan (e.g. people cut off by the tide or stuck in a rip tide). All that may be required is to inform a lifeguard, or all that may be possible is to get help.

Never attempt a rescue which may be beyond your capability as this may cause a double tragedy. As has already been said, no two drowning accidents are the same, and so the assessment and action required will differ from situation to situation. It is therefore important to practise dealing with emergency situations by taking part in initiative tests and unknown incidents with your class. It is also useful to pose yourself different problems and consider the best action for each.

Action

Once you have assessed the situation and the plan of action is determined, your action must be decisive, speedy and performed efficiently. The situation may change as you act, however, and you may have to make adjustments to your plan. For example, a casualty who was conscious may become unconscious and stop breathing.

Categories of Drowning Casualties

	CONSCIOUS			UNCONSCIOUS
	Weak swimmer	**Non-swimmer**	**Injured (swimmer or non-swimmer)**	
Position in water	Could be using legs and arms for support; the casualty is at an angle to the surface; normally facing the shoreline.	May not be using arms and legs for support; vertical in the water; not necessarily facing shoreline.	An awkward position in the water caused by grasping the injured limb or area.	Completely limp in the water; head only visible if at the surface, otherwise at any point between bottom and surface.
Attempts to attract attention	Might wave and call for help.	Seldom waves or calls for help.	Limited by nature of injury.	None
Facial expression	Varying degrees of anxiety in face and eyes.	Panic-eyes opthalmic (wide-eyed).	As for weak or non-swimmer.	Relaxed.

To ensure the maximum degree of safety for the rescuer, the possible methods of rescue should be considered in the following sequence:

Reach
Throw
Wade
Row
Swim (taking a rescue aid to a conscious casualty)
Swim and tow (when the casualty is unconscious)

Everyone can help in some way. Even a non-swimmer can reach,throw, wade, go for help or provide resuscitation and appropriate first aid.

Important Always remember that a rescuer must only enter the water as a last resort – *your safety is vital.*

What follows outlines some ways in which you might be able to help someone who is drowning.

Reaching rescues

Reaching recues are the safest method of rescue and should *always* be considered first when dealing with an emergency and used whenever possible. These techniques are particularly useful for the weak or non-swimmer who should never enter the water to rescue a

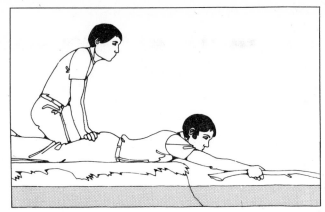

Reaching rescues

casualty. With the use of aids the distance over which one can effect a rescue will be greatly increased. An aid can be either rigid (e.g. a branch, stick or umbrella) or non-rigid (e.g. clothing, a towel or rope). It is also possible to tie two non-rigid aids together (e.g. two items of clothing) to extend the reach.

Description Select a suitable aid and attract the casualty's attention. Lie down on your front facing the casualty. Be careful not to lie any further out than chest height as you may slide, or be pulled, into the water. If possible anchor yourself firmly by holding on to a fixed object (e.g. a post, tree or railings).

If an assistant is available he should kneel between your legs and anchor you to the floor by pressing down on the back of the thighs.

Give the casualty clear instructions to hold on to the aid, pull him in steadily and secure him to the side.

Important If you are in any danger of being pulled into the water, **let go.**

Throwing rescues

This is a second set of skills which are extremely effective and can be used by the non-swimmer. They can be used when the casualty is too far away to reach, but still ensure the safety of the rescuer. Throwing rescues can be divided into two types:

1 **With a buoyant aid**
   The aid being used should have sufficient buoyancy to float *and* support the casualty (e.g. a football or lifebelt). When making a throw in open water conditions allowances must be made for such factors as wind direction, currents and tides. If it is possible to attach a line to the object it will enable it to be retrieved if the throw is inaccurate, or can be used to pull the casualty to safety.
   Description Attract the casualty's attention and indicate that you are going to throw something. Stand clear of the water's edge and throw the aid to the casualty. Aim to hit the water just in front of the casualty and within arm's length. Give the casualty clear and positive instructions to look towards the bank ('look at me') and kick hard.

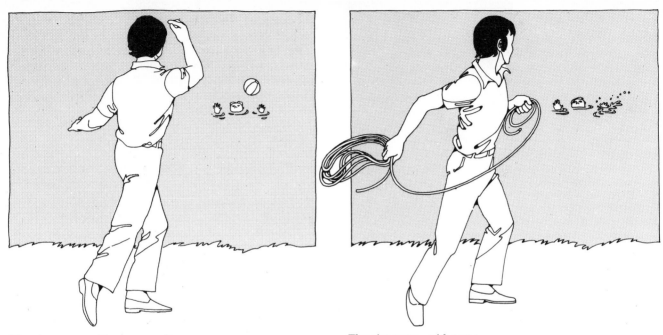

Throwing rescue – with a buoyant aid

Throwing rescue – with a rope

2   With a rope

This has the advantage of always being available for a second throw if the first is not accurate and of pulling the casualty to safety.

Description Attract the casualty's attenton, stand clear of the water's edge and coil the rope. Care should be taken when coiling the rope to avoid tangles by making uniform loops. Hold the end of

Greater accuracy can be achieved if the end of the rope is slightly weighted. Be careful to select a weight which is not likely to cause injury, preferably a buoyant aid.

Wade rescues

These can be used in shallow water when attempts to reach and throw have been unsuccessful, and when factors such as depth, current and water temperature permit a safe entry. Wading part way to a casualty can lengthen the distance over which a reach or throw can be effected.

Description Find a suitable reaching or throwing aid and reassure the casualty. 'Slide-in' the water feeling with

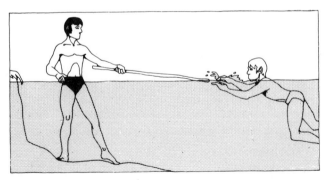

Wade rescue

the rope securely with the non-throwing hand and throw the coils as accurately as possible allowing for such factors as wind and current. Give the casualty clear instructions to hold the rope with two hands and steadily pull him in. Slow down as the casualty reaches the bank.

your feet for the bottom or any hidden obstacles. Wade by sliding your feet along the bottom very cautiously. Beware of any underwater obstructions. It is a useful idea to test the depth of the water with a pole. Reach or throw the rescue aid to the casualty and help him back without being held.

Never wade any further than waist depth and if in danger of being grasped or pulled over – **let go**.

Swimming rescues

This type of rescue is only used when all land-based rescues have either failed or are not appropriate, for example when the casualty is out of reach or unconscious. It is important that the rescuer realises his limitations both in skill and endurance, so that he does not become involved in a rescue situation that he cannot handle.

It is, therefore, only as a last resort that the *trained* rescuer will perform a swimming rescue. There are three types of swim rescue to be considered, in the following order of priority –

1   Accompanied rescue.

2   Non-contact rescue.

3   Contact rescue.

Contact rescues should only be used when they are absolutely necessary (e.g. when the casualty is unconscious) as they endanger the safety of the rescuer. Rarely will there be a situation where no aids are available and contact rescues should not be used except by those who are highly trained.

The rescuer must consider the distance and water conditions before deciding on what clothing to remove. It may be necessary to remove heavy top clothing but in open water clothing will protect a rescuer from the effects of cold and hypothermia. In some situations light footwear is an advantage as it can protect the rescuer's feet.

Towing aids should be taken whenever possible; buoyant ones are the best but they are not always available; clothing is always available.

During the swim out the rescuer should try and keep the casualty in sight, and a balance should be struck between the need for speed in the swim out and the need to conserve energy for the difficult return journey. Rescuers should use a stroke which enables them to observe the casualty. The final approach should be carried out with the head up and with great caution; breast stroke is best at this stage.

There must be a continuous reassessment of the situation and conditions throughout the rescue sequence, so that the rescuer does not himself become a casualty.

1 Accompanied rescue

A competent swimmer can offer assistance by swimming out with a buoyant aid that will provide support and accompanying the casualty to safety, without risking direct contact.

Description Select a buoyant aid that will provide support (e.g. a football, or lifebelt) and enter the water by an appropriate method (see page 9/10). Approach and instruct the casualty what to do. Pass the aid to the casualty, *keeping at a safe distance*, to avoid being grasped. Tell him to kick his legs and accompany him to safety. Encourage gentle movements initially to develop confidence and stability. Always encourage and give 'positive' instructions. If the casualty is having difficulty making headway back to the shore stand by and give encouragement until help arrives.

2 Non-contact rescue

If after taking hold of the supporting aid the casualty is unable to make progress then the rescuer may take hold of the support and tow the casualty to safety.

There may be times when a buoyant support is not available, but the rescuer should never need to resort to taking hold of the conscious casualty as there will always be something available to use as a towing aid with which to effect a non-contact rescue.

In an emergency any aid may be used but some things are better than others. Ideally the aid should be buoyant enough to support the rescuer and casualty if necessary; about one metre long, to ensure a 'safe' distance between rescuer and

Accompanied rescue

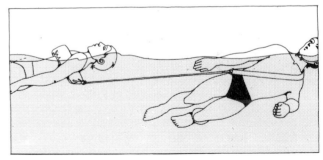

Non-contact rescue

casualty, giving the rescuer time to get clear if the casualty panics; and rigid, to allow the casualty to lever himself against it and make it easier to keep his head above water.

Description Select a suitable towing aid and enter the water as appropriate for the conditions (see page 9/10). Stay at least two metres away whilst instructing the casualty and pass the aid when you are sure it is safe. Get the casualty to hold the aid with two hands, turn over on his back and hold the aid close to his chest.

Tow the casualty, keeping your arm straight to avoid jerkiness, and swim side stroke to watch the casualty . Be ready to release the aid if the casualty attempts to grasp you.

3 Contact rescue

These should only be used when the casualty is unconscious, persistently refuses an aid or when all other types of rescue are impossible.

As any rescuer effecting a contact rescue should be highly trained the only tow which will be outlined in this section will be the Extended Tow which can be used if the casualty is unconscious. Further information regarding contact rescues can be obtained from the *RLSS Handbook*, Section 2, 'Water Rescue Skills', or by joining your local lifesaving class.

Extended tow

This tow can be used when the casualty is unconscious or passive and co-operative, in calm water.

Description Take hold from the rear of the casualty's chin, hair or clothing, taking care not to impede the airway. Use side stroke or lifesaving backstroke and keep your arm straight and directly in line over your body. Maintain a constant check on the casualty to ensure water is not passing over his face.

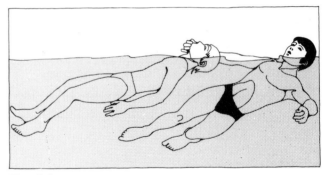

Extended tow

Landings

A number of factors existing at the time of an emergency will dictate the method necessary to land the casualty.

1 The rescuer – his strength, height, experience and energy.
2 The casualty – conscious or unconscious, height and weight, injuries.
3 The conditions – beach, boat, steep bank.

The following are some of the landing techniques which can be adapted to cater for all casualties and all conditions.

Support

This is used to secure the casualty in a position of safety against a firm support with his face out of the water, and if the rescuer is too exhausted, or not strong enough, to land the casualty until assistance is at hand.

Description On making contact with the point of support, turn the casualty to face the bank between you and the side. Pass your arms one at a time under the casualty's armpits and take a firm grip on the available support. If required provide added support by placing your knee between his thighs, against the bank. If the casualty cannot support his head incline it back to rest on your shoulder.

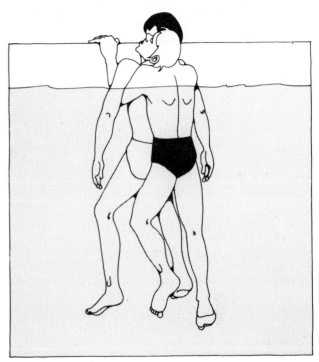

Support

The Stirrup Landing

This method can be used when the casualty is able to help and can be assisted out of the water.

Description Support the casualty against the bank, instruct him. Reach down, cup your free hand (in deep water) or both hands (in shallow water), for his foot. Lift as the casualty steps up onto the bank.

The Unassisted Lift

This technique can be used for both a conscious or unconscious casualty when no assistance from either the casualty or bystanders is available.

Description Secure the casualty by placing both his hands on the bank, holding them in place with your hand. Climb out maintaining your hold on the casualty. Take hold of the casualty's wrists, *without* crossing his or your arms. Keeping a straight back lift the casualty until his hips are level with the bank. Step back with one foot to 'fold' the casualty over the edge and allow his head to rest on your thigh. Lower him to the ground and turning his face towards you, lift his legs clear of the water onto the bank.

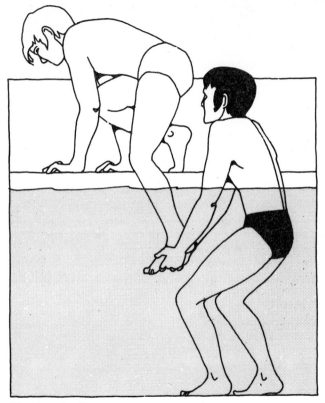

The stirrup landing

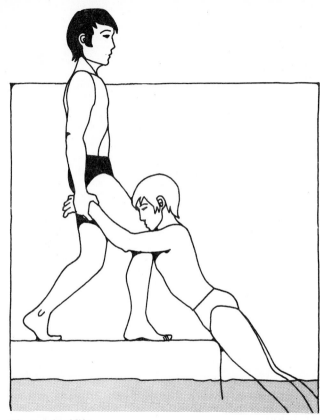

The unassisted lift

Resuscitation and Aftercare

A casualty who is unconscious and not breathing requires resuscitation. Resuscitation should be given as soon as the casualty is in a secure position. Even non-swimmers can help with this and should learn the techniques.

Resuscitation is the act of revival of a nearly, or apparently, dead person. The techniques of resuscitation include opening the airway and artificial ventilation.

The most effective method of providing artificial ventilation is the Expired Air method. It has been shown conclusively that this is the *only* really efficient method without apparatus and provides:

1 Effective pulmonary ventilation.
2 Ease of learning and practice.
3 Simplicity in operation.
4 A technique that will not cause injury.

The golden rules for resuscitation are:
1 Keep calm.
2 Start as soon as possible.
3 Send for help if possible.

Expired Air Resuscitation (EAR)

This method provides better ventilation than any other method, that is, air can be got into the lungs of the casualty faster and in greater quantities than any other method. It can be started at an early stage of rescuing a drowning person, for example in the water, and can be carried out by a single operator. It is easy to teach, even to children. No aids are necessary in its execution and both hands are free to ensure a clear airway.

Diagnosis of breathing having stopped
Apart from the obvious lack of chest movement it is sometimes possible to detect the absence of breathing by the bluish discolouration of the face, lips, ears and nails (cyanosis) which results from the lack of circulating oxygenated blood.

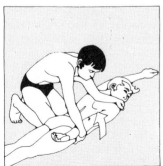

Roll the casualty onto his back

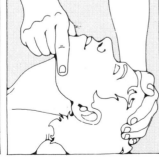

Lift the jaw and tilt the head back

Obtaining an airway
1 Place the person who has stopped breathing on his back. If he is lying on his front kneel by his side and place the nearest arm to you above his head. Turn his head to face away from you. Grasp his far shoulder with one hand and his hip with the other, clamping his wrist to his hip with your wrist. With a *steady* pull roll him over against your thighs.
   Check his mouth for obstructions.
   Lower him gently to the ground supporting his head and shoulders as you do so. Replace his arm at his side.
2 Lift his jaw and tilt his head back as far as is *reasonably* possible. The casualty may now start to breathe; if so, place him in the recovery position.
3 If he does not start breathing check that nothing is blocking the throat and start resuscitation.

Mouth-to-nose resuscitation
1 Lift the jaw and tilt the head back again.
2 Keep the casualty's mouth closed, seal your mouth over his nose and give four quick breaths. Watch for the chest to rise as this will show you are getting air into his lungs.
3 Raise your head to allow the casualty to breathe out,

turning your head towards the chest (watch for it to fall).

4 Repeat the sequence with *one* inflation *every five seconds*.

5 Keep performing EAR until the casualty starts to breathe again. This may be a *very* long time but *do not stop until a doctor or an ambulance arrives*.

Mouth-to-mouth resuscitation

If the mouth-to-nose method does not make the chest rise the nose may be blocked so try the mouth-to-mouth method. This technique is exactly the same as the mouth-to-nose method explained above, except that you pinch the nose and make a seal with your mouth over the casualty's mouth.

Resuscitation of babies

If the casualty is a baby place your mouth over its mouth *and* nose. Puff air gently from your cheeks instead of taking deep breaths from your lungs and repeat this every two or three seconds.

Action for vomit

If the casualty begins to vomit quickly turn him on his side. This should be done *immediately* to prevent the stomach contents being inhaled, causing the casualty to choke.

Afterwards clear the mouth and throat and re-start resuscitation.

Post-resuscitation aftercare

When the casualty has started breathing he should be

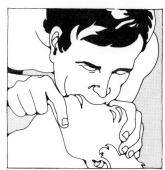

Mouth-to-mouth resuscitation

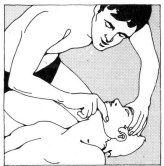

Mouth-to-nose resuscitation: step 3

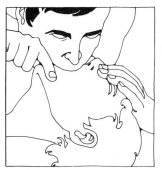

Mouth-to-nose resuscitation: step 2

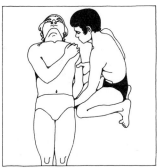

Post-resuscitation aftercare: step 2

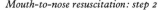

33

placed in the recovery position. Do not try to awaken an unconscious person, he is in a coma not merely a deep sleep. To turn the casualty into the recovery position:

1 Draw the casualty's forearm across his upper chest.
2 Tuck the hand of his nearest arm under his buttock.
3 Take a firm grip of his far hip and shoulder and roll him carefully towards you. Support his head to prevent it from striking the ground.
4 Allow his body to rest against your thighs as you lower him carefully to the ground.
5 Place the upper arm perpendicular to his body to support the chest and to keep it clear of the ground.
6 Draw the upper leg perpendicular to the body to support the hips and to keep the stomach clear of the ground.

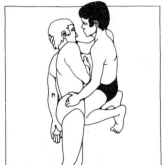
Post-resuscitation aftercare: step 3

Post-resuscitation aftercare: step 8

7 Adjust the lower arm so that it is behind and close to the body.
8 Keep the airway clear by tilting the head back holding the jaw forward and mouth open.

Always keep a casualty who had stopped breathing and undergone resuscitation under close observation as it may be necessary to restart resuscitation.

Medical help

A casualty who has required resuscitation must *be taken to a hospital as soon as possible whether he has recovered consciousness or not. Keep the casualty in the recovery position during removal to hospital.*

Practising expired air resuscitation

1 Practise breathing deeply at five-second intervals.
2 Learn to put the head in the correct position by practising with a partner.
3 Get used to adopting the correct position for the operator by kneeling close to your partner.
4 Practise whenever possible on a manikin or mask.
5 For practice or demonstration purposes, where a training aid is not available, lean over your partner and breathe down past his far cheek.
6 Practise turning your partner into the position for resuscitation and the recovery position.

Be Prepared

To be thoroughly prepared to rescue a person you must be properly taught and trained. The best way to do this is to join a local lifesaving club or class, learn from the experts and take a proficiency test to prove your ability.

It is important that even the most highly qualified life saver should keep in practice and take a repeat test or train for a higher Award. Practise with others in staged incidents and initiative tests is invaluable. However, it is always wise to practise any water skills in the presence of a qualified lifesaver in case an accident occurs.

Teaching Programmes and Awards

There are a number of RLSS Awards which can be taken by individuals who wish to test their knowledge. These also serve as a useful introduction to the more advanced Awards (see diagram on p.40). All the Society's Awards are described in the *RLSS Handbook*, Section 6, 'The Awards Schemes', together with the detailed regulations for all RLSS Awards.

Examinations can be arranged locally, and application should be made to the local Area Organiser or Branch Secretary. The name and address of your local Branch Secretary is available from RLSS Headquarters, Mountbatten House, Studley, Warwickshire, B80 7NN.

These Awards, details of which are given below, provide a useful introduction to lifesaving skills and can be taken by people whether or not they are RLSS members.

AQUAPACK

For the first time a wide range of water safety, safer swimming and water rescue skills have been brought together in one scheme. So whether you are a non-swimmer or swimmer, a performer or teacher, handicapped or able-bodied, old or young, the new AQUAPACK programme has something for you.

The keys to taking part in the scheme are the AQUAPACKS. These are personal log books which enable each person taking part to plot their own progress through the skills in each award and get their Certificates signed as soon as they have passed. With each AQUAPACK comes a 'Blue Code' for Water Safety to ensure that everyone taking part has the information necessary to help them become safer around water.

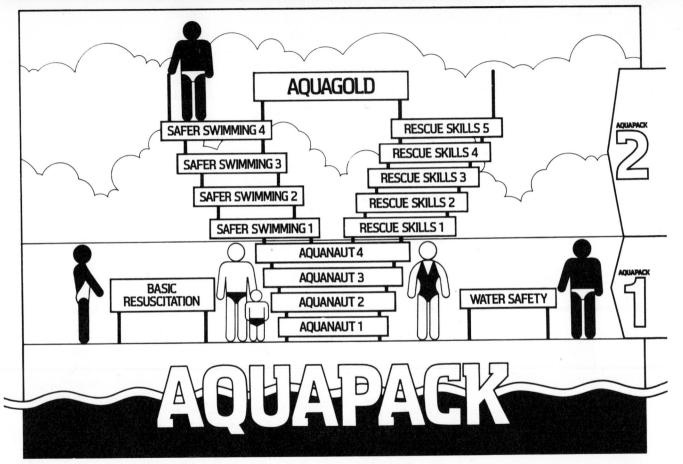

AQUAGOLD

SAFER SWIMMING 4
SAFER SWIMMING 3
SAFER SWIMMING 2
SAFER SWIMMING 1

RESCUE SKILLS 5
RESCUE SKILLS 4
RESCUE SKILLS 3
RESCUE SKILLS 2
RESCUE SKILLS 1

AQUANAUT 4
AQUANAUT 3
AQUANAUT 2
AQUANAUT 1

BASIC RESUSCITATION

WATER SAFETY

AQUAPACK 2

AQUAPACK 1

AQUAPACK

AQUAPACK 1 is for swimmers *and* non swimmers alike; through the Water Safety, AQUANAUT and Basic Resuscitation awards, it provides all the skills needed to start on the road to being safer in and around water. AQUAPACK 2, aimed at the better swimmer, includes awards for Safer Swimming and Rescue Skills; the AQUAGOLD award marks the completion of both.

Candidates can start on the scheme either by passing the Water Safety Award (for which they receive a woven badge and AQUAPACK 1) or by purchasing either AQUAPACK 1 or 2 depending on their ability level.

b) mouth to nose resuscitation

c) action which would be taken if the casualty were to vomit.

3   Using a length of wood, demonstrate a reaching rescue.

4   Using two articles of clothing tied together, demonstrate a reaching rescue.

5   Throw an unweighted rope to within reach of a stationary casualty over a distance of 6 metres.

6   Throw a buoyant aid (e.g. football or airtight container) to within reach of a stationary casualty over a distance of 6 metres.

Water Safety Award

Aim: to introduce water safety knowledge and skills.

1   Show a knowledge of water safety by answering 4 questions drawn from the 'Blue Code' for Water Safety.

2   Demonstrate the technique of Expired Air Resuscitation (kiss of life) showing:

a) how to tilt the head back to make a clear airway

Basic Resuscitation Award

Aim: to introduce resuscitation to younger candidates as a preparation for formal lifesaving training and higher resuscitation tests.

1   Demonstrate to the satisfaction of the examiner the expired air method showing:
    a) the correct positioning of the casualty
    b) the mouth to nose technique
    c) the mouth to mouth technique
    d) action to be taken in case of the casualty vomiting
    e) placing the casualty in the recovery position.
2   Answer three questions on the techniques demonstrated.

Want to take part?

As a candidate – if you are a member of a club, youth group or school, ask your leader/teacher, or look for this sign at your local pool . . .

As a teacher – get more information by contacting RLSS Headquarters at the address and telephone number below, and all the information you require to start the scheme will be sent to you by return.

The Royal Life Saving Society
Mountbatten House
Studley
Warwickshire B80 7NN
Tel: Studley (STD 052 785) 3943

surface dive
underwater swimming
swimming strokes – head up on the front
lifesaving backstroke

RLSS Elementary Award

Aim: to test self-preservation, swimming competence and non-contact rescue at a preparatory stage to higher awards. The holder is *not* qualified to attempt a swimming rescue in deep water.
Award: woven badge.
Age limit: none.
Examiners: the examination shall be conducted by one RLSS Grade 3 examiner.
Dress for water test: candidate and casualty – swimwear.

Syllabus of skills for water test
The contents of this award have been designed to test a selection of the following skills:

> reaching rescue
> throwing rescue – buoyant aid
> wading rescue
> human chain
> entries – shallow water
> shallow water exits
> accompanied rescue
> assisted landings

Examination
Details of this are available from RLSS local branches (addresses can be obtained from Headquarters).

The examination will consist of three sections:—

1   questions on water safety

2   resuscitation test

3   water test

1. **Water Safety and Rescue**   Answer 6 questions on water safety from the "Blue Code" for Water Safety.

2. **Resuscitation**   Successfully complete the examination for the Basic Resuscitation Award.

3. **Water Test**   a) This test represents a situation where your friend who is a non-swimmer has slipped and fallen into the water. The casualty will be in deep water, one metre from the side – demonstrate a reaching rescue and instruct him/her how to climb out.
b) The current has taken your friend a little further from the side, and he/she is in deep water 8 metres away from

you – demonstrate a throwing rescue using a buoyant aid and secure him/her in a position of safety. You will be allowed only one attempt to reach the casualty.

c) You do not know the depth and conditions of the water. Taking a pole, test the depth, enter the water, and wade near enough to the casualty to reach him/her using the pole. Return the casualty to your point of entry. For test purposes, the casualty will be 4 metres away from the bank (at the shallow end of a swimming pool).

d) An aid that will float is available, and you are a swimmer. The casualty is in deep water 20 metres away from your entry point into shallow water. Demonstrate how the buoyant aid can be used to rescue the casualty by an accompanied rescue. He/she should be brought back 20 metres to your entry point, and assisted to land.

e) This test represents a situation where a casualty has sunk to the bottom and you are helping in the search. Enter the water, swim 10 metres and demonstrate a feet first surface dive to the bottom, which shall be 1.5m deep. Swim for two strokes underwater with body and limbs fully submerged before surfacing and return to your point of entry using lifesaving backstroke.

f) As a test of your swimming ability, swim continuously for 125m of which:

i) 75m is head up on the front

ii) 50m is lifesaving backstroke without the use of arms.

RLSS Intermediate Award

Aim: to test the ability of the more competent swimmer at a stage preparatory to the Bronze Medallion. The holder is *not* qualified to attempt a contact rescue in deep water.

Award: woven badge.

Age limit: none.

Examiners: the examination shall be conducted by one RLSS Grade 3 examiner.

Dress for water test: candidate and casualty – swimwear.

Syllabus of skills for water test

The contents of this award have been designed to test a selection from the following skills:

    reaching rescue
    throwing rescues
    wading rescue
    human chain
    entry – shallow water
    straddle jump

accompanied rescue
non-contact rescue
support position
assisted landing – shallow and deep water
conducting a search
surface dive
recovery of an object
shallow water resuscitation
contact tow – unconscious casualty
recovery position
defences
swimming strokes – head up on the front
                       side stroke
                       lifesaving backstroke

Examination

The examination will consist of three sections:—

1 questions on water safety and rescue
2 resuscitation test
3 water test

1. Water Safety and Rescue   Answer 6 questions on water safety and the principles and methods of rescue from Section 1 of the Society's Handbook 'Life Saving and Water Safety – an Introduction', and the Blue Code for Water Safety.

2. Resuscitation   Successfully complete the examination for the Basic Resuscitation Award.

3. Water Test   a) This test represents a situation where your friend who is a non-swimmer has slipped and fallen into the water. The casualty will be in deep water, 2 metres from the side – demonstrate a reaching rescue using a rigid aid and instruct him/her how to climb out.

b) The current has taken your friend a little further from the side, and he/she is in deep water 8 metres away from you – demonstrate a throwing rescue using an unweighted rope and instruct the casualty how to climb out. You will be allowed up to three attempts to reach the casualty.

c) You do not know the depth and condition of the water. Taking a pole, test the depth, enter the water, and wade near enough to the casualty to reach him/her using the pole. Return the casualty to your point of entry and secure in the support position. For test purposes, the casualty will be 6 metres away from the side (at the shallow end of a swimming pool).

d) An aid that will float is available, and you are a swimmer. A weak swimmer is in difficulties in deep water 20 metres away. Enter deep water with a straddle jump, demonstrate how the buoyant aid can be used to rescue the casualty by an accompanied rescue. Accompany 20 metres back to your entry point and assist to land.

e) A non-swimmer is in difficulty in deep water 25 metres away. A rigid buoyant aid is available. Enter shallow water and demonstrate how the aid can be used to rescue the casualty by a non-contact rescue. Tow him/her 25 metres back to your entry point and secure in the support position.

f) Enter shallow water and conduct a search for a casualty known to be on the bottom approximately 15 metres away from your point of entry. During the search, demonstrate a head first surface dive. Recover the casualty and tow to water shallow enough to enable you to perform resuscitation. Commence resuscitation and, with the aid of an assistant, land the casualty. On landing, the casualty will be considered to have re-commenced breathing. Place in the recovery position. An object (2–4 kilos) will be placed at a depth of 1.5m to represent the casualty. A casualty will be substituted for the object on reaching the surface.

g) To demonstrate the action that might have to be taken in a surprise situation, the candidate will demonstrate two defence actions as specified by the examiner.

h) Swim continuously for 150 metres, of which:
 i) 50m is head up on the front
 ii) 50 m is side stroke
 iii) 50m is lifesaving backstroke without the use of arms.
The time limit for this test is 4 minutes.

The RLSS Lifeguards

Those who have qualified in the RLSS Bronze Medallion, or higher, and who wish to use their skills and knowledge in giving service to the community, may like to join the lifeguards. The Society registers over a hundred voluntary lifeguard units whose members give up their time, freely, to make the waterways a safer place.

Lifeguards work as a team and enjoy comradeship as members of a club. They provide teams to man popular bathing places both at the sea and inland at weekends and on public holidays. Many of them have up-to-date equipment including two-way radios and engine-powered patrol boats.

While much has been done towards providing a nationwide service more volunteers and new clubs are needed. The basic requirements of membership are:

1 Lifeguards may be men or women but must be members of Lifeguard Clubs recognised by the Society. They must hold a current Bronze Medallion and be over 18, or hold the Award of Merit and be over 16.

2 Cadets must hold the Bronze Medallion.

3 Associate members of Clubs may be those in training to become qualified or those who help with administration.

Further information on lifeguarding and establishing a lifeguard club is available in the *RLSS Handbook*, Section 7, 'Lifeguard Manual'. For details of your local lifeguard club, and RLSS publications, contact either your local RLSS Branch Secretary or the Society's Headquarters, Mountbatten House, Studley, Warwickshire, B80 7NN.

Index